# The Thinking Tree

# BOOK OF

# STATE TREES

## Nature Study Handbook

Learning about the botanical trees for all **50 US** States, locating their scientific names, research projects, creative activities, and more!

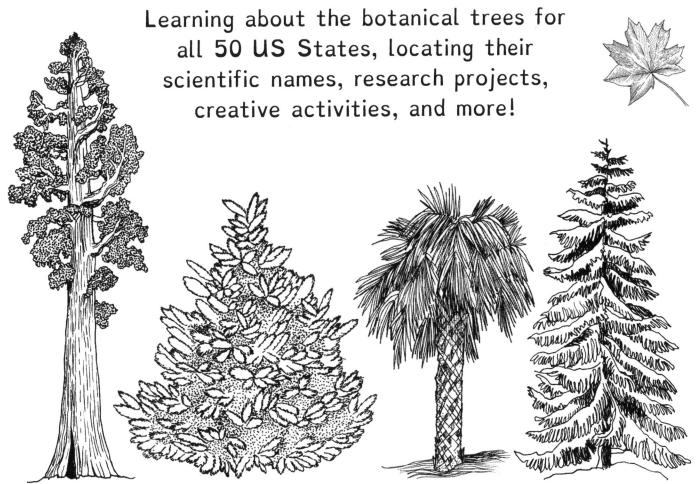

WRITTEN AND DESIGNED BY:
NORA McCAIN APPLE

Illustrations/Artwork by: Anna Kidalova
Cover Artwork by: Sarah Janisse Brown

# FUNSCHOOLING.COM

# THE THINKING TREE, LLC

My name is: _____

_____

Date: _____

Age: _____

# Instructions:

**Botany** is the science of plants, flowers, and trees. Botany is a branch of biology, one of the living sciences. A scientist, or plant scientist, who specializes in the field of botany, is called a *botanist*.

Humans began studying plants as far back as Adam and Eve. It was necessary to identify which trees could be used for shade, building houses, canoes, furniture, etc. Today, botanists study approximately **410,000** species of plants!

This workbook will include science, geography, history, language arts, and creative arts all in one! If you are using the book for school, work on one page a day, or as many as you want to fit into your curriculum. The vocabulary words are located at the beginning so you will understand the terms when you research each state tree.

This is a workbook purposed to develop research skills. Think of all the different ways to research the tree species. Use a dictionary in book form to look up and learn the vocabulary words. Have your parent help with any searches on the Internet or schedule a library day to research the information. Choose your favorite reading spot, such as a beanbag chair, comfy desk, or under your favorite oak tree. Be sure to have colored pencils, pens, or markers ready to doodle and practice your art skills!

I know you will have fun learning about our amazing botanical Earth!

# UNITED STATES OF AMERICA

Find and color your state!

What State do you live in? _____

Here are some helpful websites for your parents to help with your research:

- https://www.50states.com/tree/
- https://state.1keydata.com/state-trees.php
- https://statesymbolsusa.org/categories/state-tree
- https://en.wikipedia.org/wiki/List_of_U.S._state_and_territory_trees
- https://www.mnn.com/earth-matters/wilderness-resources/photos/most-endangered-trees-america/close-extinction

# VOCABULARY WORDS

abscission: _____
_____
_____

biology: _____
_____
_____

botany: _____
_____
_____

coniferous: _____
_____
_____

deciduous: _____
_____
_____

ecology: _____
_____
_____

# VOCABULARY WORDS

evergreen: _____

_____

_____

hardwood: _____

_____

_____

indigenous: _____

_____

_____

native: _____

_____

_____

pollen: _____

_____

_____

softwood: _____

_____

_____

# ALABAMA

The state tree is: **Longleaf Pine**

Find the botanical name: _____

   List any other names by which this tree is known:

_____

Is this tree deciduous or coniferous (evergreen)? _____

Does this tree produce flowers? _____ Which season? _____

   Does this tree produce fruit? _____ What kind? _____

Is this tree's trunk hardwood or softwood? _____

List some items made from the wood of this state tree: _____

_____

_____

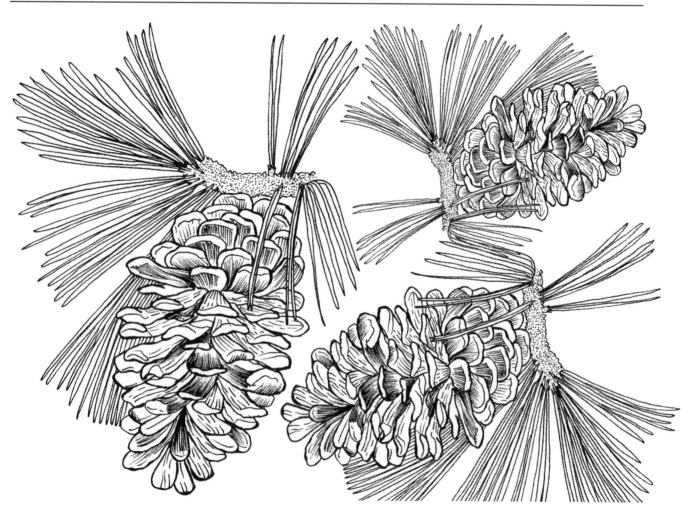

Find this state on page 5 and use a different color to fill it in.

What is the capital city of this state?
_____

# CREATIVE WRITING

In the space below, write a poem, short story, or a unique history tid-bit about the state tree. If this tree is in your state, and in season, try taping a leaf to this page and press it in the book!

_____
_____
_____
_____
_____
_____
_____
_____

List the different colors of this tree in each season:

Winter: _____

Spring: _____

Summer: _____

Autumn: _____

How tall does this tree grow?
_____

What is the average diameter of the tree's trunk?
_____

What is the average lifespan of this tree?
_____

List the sources you used to research this tree:

Books: _____

Websites: _____

Other sources: _____
_____

# ALASKA

The state tree is: **Sitka Spruce**

Find the botanical name: _____

   List any other names by which this tree is known: _____

_____

Is this tree deciduous or coniferous (evergreen)? _____

Does this tree produce flowers? _____ Which season? _____

   Does this tree produce fruit? _____ What kind? _____

Is this tree's trunk hardwood or softwood? _____

List some items made from the wood of this state tree: _____

_____

**Fun fact:**
The Sitka spruce tree is the tallest conifer in the world.

Find this state on page **5** and use a different color to fill it in.

What is the capital city of this state?

_____

# CREATIVE WRITING

In the space below, write a poem, short story, or a unique history tid-bit about the state tree. If this tree is in your state, and in season, try taping a leaf to this page and press it in the book!

_____

_____

_____

_____

_____

_____

_____

_____

List the different colors of this tree in each season:

**Winter:** _____

**Spring:** _____

**Summer:** _____

**Autumn:** _____

How tall does this tree grow?

_____

What is the average diameter of the tree's trunk?

_____

What is the average lifespan of this tree?

_____

List the sources you used to research this tree:

Books: _____

_____

Websites: _____

Other sources: _____

_____

# ARIZONA

The state tree is: **Palo Verde**

Find the botanical name: _____

List any other names by which this tree is known: _____

_____

Is this tree deciduous or coniferous (evergreen)? _____

Does this tree produce flowers? _____ Which season? _____

Does this tree produce fruit? _____ What kind? _____

Is this tree's trunk hardwood or softwood? _____

List some items made from the wood of this state tree: _____

_____

_____

Fun fact:
"Palo Verde" in Spanish
means "green stick."

12

Find this state on page **5** and use a different color to fill it in.

What is the capital city of this state?

_____

# CREATIVE WRITING

In the space below, write a poem, short story, or a unique history tid-bit about the state tree. If this tree is in your state, and in season, try taping a leaf to this page and press it in the book!

_____

_____

_____

_____

_____

_____

_____

_____

List the different colors of this tree in each season:

**Winter:** _____

**Spring:** _____

**Summer:** _____

**Autumn:** _____

How tall does this tree grow?

_____

What is the average diameter of the tree's trunk?

_____

What is the average lifespan of this tree?

_____

List the sources you used to research this tree:

Books: _____

_____

Websites: _____

_____

Other sources: _____

_____

# ARKANSAS

The state tree is: **Loblolly Pine**

Find the botanical name: _____

List any other names by which this tree is known: _____

_____

Is this tree deciduous or coniferous (evergreen)? _____

Does this tree produce flowers? _____ Which season? _____

Does this tree produce fruit? _____ What kind? _____

Is this tree's trunk hardwood or softwood? _____

List some items made from the wood of this state tree: _____

_____

_____

Find this state on page **5** and use a different color to fill it in.

What is the capital city of this state?

_____

# CREATIVE WRITING

In the space below, write a poem, short story, or a unique history tid-bit about the state tree. If this tree is in your state, and in season, try taping a leaf to this page and press it in the book!

_____

_____

_____

_____

_____

_____

_____

_____

List the different colors of this tree in each season:

**Winter:** _____

**Spring:** _____

**Summer:** _____

**Autumn:** _____

How tall does this tree grow?

_____

What is the average diameter of the tree's trunk?

_____

What is the average lifespan of this tree?

_____

List the sources you used to research this tree:

Books: _____

_____

Websites: _____

_____

Other sources: _____

_____

# CALIFORNIA

The state trees are:

## California Redwood and Giant Sequoia

Find the botanical name for the California Redwood:

_____

Find the botanical name for the Giant Sequoia:

_____

Are these trees included in the Endangered Trees list? _____

Is this tree's trunk hardwood or softwood? _____

List some items made from the wood of this state tree: _____

_____

_____

Find this state on page **5** and use a different color to fill it in.

What is the capital city of this state?

_____

# CREATIVE WRITING

In the space below, write a poem, short story, or a unique history tid-bit about the state tree. If this tree is in your state, and in season, try taping a leaf to this page and press it in the book!

_____

_____

_____

_____

_____

_____

_____

List the different colors of this tree in each season:

**Winter:** _____

**Spring:** _____

**Summer:** _____

**Autumn:** _____

How tall does this tree grow?

_____

What is the average diameter of the tree's trunk?

_____

What is the average lifespan of this tree?

_____

List the sources you used to research this tree:

Books: _____

_____

Websites: _____

_____

Other sources: _____

_____

# CREATIVE ARTS

Fill in the missing parts. Write the name of each tree from this section:

# CREATIVE ARTS

Draw your favorite tree from this section. Use your imagination to draw the tree in its natural habitat. Add a house, forest, or animals!

# COLORADO

The state tree is: Colorado Blue Spruce

Find the botanical name: _____

   List any other names by which this tree is known: _____

_____

Is this tree deciduous or coniferous (evergreen)? _____

Does this tree produce flowers? _____ Which season? _____

   Does this tree produce fruit? _____ What kind? _____

Is this tree's trunk hardwood or softwood? _____

List some items made from the wood of this state tree: _____

_____

_____

Fun fact:
The Blue Spruce can withstand extremely low temperatures, as low as −40°!

20

Find this state on page **5** and use a different color to fill it in.

What is the capital city of this state?
_____

# CREATIVE WRITING

In the space below, write a poem, short story, or a unique history tid-bit about the state tree. If this tree is in your state, and in season, try taping a leaf to this page and press it in the book!

_____
_____
_____
_____
_____
_____
_____
_____

List the different colors of this tree in each season:

Winter: _____

Spring: _____

Summer: _____

Autumn: _____

How tall does this tree grow?
_____

What is the average diameter of the tree's trunk?
_____

What is the average lifespan of this tree?
_____

List the sources you used to research this tree:

Books: _____

Websites: _____

Other sources: _____
_____

# CONNECTICUT

The state tree is: **White Oak**

Find the botanical name: _____

List any other names by which this tree is known: _____
_____

Is this tree deciduous or coniferous (evergreen)? _____

Does this tree produce flowers? _____ Which season? _____

Does this tree produce fruit? _____ What kind? _____

Is this tree's trunk hardwood or softwood? _____

List some items made from the wood of this state tree: _____
_____
_____

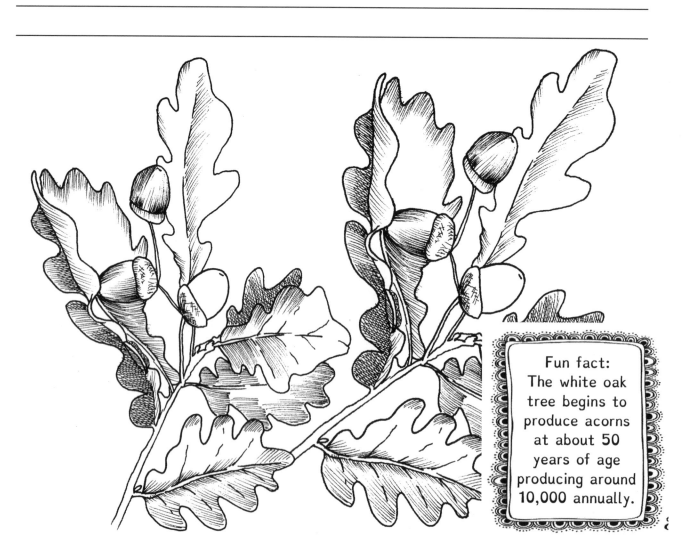

Fun fact:
The white oak tree begins to produce acorns at about **50** years of age producing around **10,000** annually.

Find this state on page **5** and use a different color to fill it in.

What is the capital city of this state?

_____

# CREATIVE WRITING

In the space below, write a poem, short story, or a unique history tid-bit about the state tree. If this tree is in your state, and in season, try taping a leaf to this page and press it in the book!

_____

_____

_____

_____

_____

_____

_____

_____

List the different colors of this tree in each season:

**Winter:** _____

**Spring:** _____

**Summer:** _____

**Autumn:** _____

How tall does this tree grow?

_____

What is the average diameter of the tree's trunk?

_____

What is the average lifespan of this tree?

_____

List the sources you used to research this tree:

Books: _____

Websites: _____

Other sources: _____

# DELAWARE

The state tree is: *American Holly Tree*

Find the botanical name: _____

    List any other names by which this tree is known:

_____

Is this tree deciduous or coniferous (evergreen)? _____

Does this tree produce flowers? _____ Which season? _____

    Does this tree produce fruit? _____ What kind? _____

Is this tree's trunk hardwood or softwood? _____

List some items made from the wood of this state tree: _____

_____

_____

Fun fact:
The flowers are pollinated by insects, and the berries are poisonous to humans but are survival food for birds!

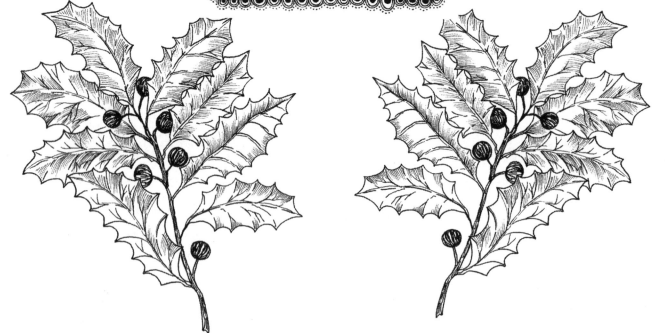

Find this state on page **5** and use a different color to fill it in.

What is the capital city of this state?

_____

# CREATIVE WRITING

In the space below, write a poem, short story, or a unique history tid-bit about the state tree. If this tree is in your state, and in season, try taping a leaf to this page and press it in the book!

_____

_____

_____

_____

_____

_____

_____

_____

List the different colors of this tree in each season:

Winter: _____

Spring: _____

Summer: _____

Autumn: _____

How tall does this tree grow?

_____

What is the average diameter of the tree's trunk?

_____

What is the average lifespan of this tree?

_____

List the sources you used to research this tree:

Books: _____

Websites: _____

Other sources: _____

_____

# FLORIDA

The state tree is: **Sabal Palm**

Find the botanical name: _____

List any other names by which this tree is

_____

Is this tree deciduous or coniferous (evergreen)? _____

Does this tree produce flowers? _____ Which season? _____

Does this tree produce fruit? _____ What kind? _____

Is this tree's trunk hardwood or softwood? _____

List some items made from the wood of this state tree: _____

_____

_____

By what kind of water
does the Sabal Palm
love to grow?

_____

Find this state on page **5** and use a different color to fill it in.

What is the capital city of this state?

_____

## CREATIVE WRITING

In the space below, write a poem, short story, or a unique history tid-bit about the state tree. If this tree is in your state, and in season, try taping a leaf to this page and press it in the book!

_____

_____

_____

_____

_____

_____

_____

List the different colors of this tree in each season:

Winter: _____

Spring: _____

Summer: _____

Autumn: _____

How tall does this tree grow?

_____

What is the average diameter of the tree's trunk?

_____

What is the average lifespan of this tree?

_____

List the sources you used to research this tree:

Books: _____

_____

Websites: _____

_____

Other sources: _____

_____

# GEORGIA

The state tree is: **Live Oak**

Find the botanical name: _____

List any other names by which this tree is know

_____

Is this tree deciduous or coniferous (evergreen)? _____

Does this tree produce flowers? _____ Which season? _____

Does this tree produce fruit? _____ What kind? _____

Is this tree's trunk hardwood or softwood? _____

List some items made from the wood of this state tree: _____

_____

_____

Find this state on page **5** and use a different color to fill it in.

What is the capital city of this state?

_____

## CREATIVE WRITING

In the space below, write a poem, short story, or a unique history tid-bit about the state tree. If this tree is in your state, and in season, try taping a leaf to this page and press it in the book!

_____

_____

_____

_____

_____

_____

List the different colors of this tree in each season:

**Winter:** _____

**Spring:** _____

**Summer:** _____

**Autumn:** _____

How tall does this tree grow?

_____

What is the average diameter of the tree's trunk?

_____

What is the average lifespan of this tree?

_____

List the sources you used to research this tree:

Books: _____

Websites: _____

Other sources: _____

_____

# CREATIVE ARTS

Fill in the missing parts. Write the name of each tree from this section:

# CREATIVE ARTS

Draw your favorite tree from this section. Use your imagination to draw the tree in its natural habitat. Add a house, forest, or animals!

# HAWAII

The state tree is:

## Kukui Nut (Candlenut Tree)

Find the botanical name: _____

List any other names by which this tree is known: _____

_____

Is this tree deciduous or coniferous (evergreen)? _____

Does this tree produce flowers? _____ Which season? _____

Does this tree produce fruit? _____ What kind? _____

Is this tree's trunk hardwood or softwood? _____

List some items made from the wood of this state tree: _____

_____

_____

**Fun fact:**
In ancient Hawaii, the nuts of the kukui were strung in a row on a palm leaf midrib, lit on one end, and burned one by one every fifteen minutes to provide light, and to use as a measure of time.

Find this state on page **5** and use a different color to fill it in.

What is the capital city of this state?

_____

# ✳ CREATIVE WRITING ✳

In the space below, write a poem, short story, or a unique history tid-bit about the state tree. If this tree is in your state, and in season, try taping a leaf to this page and press it in the book!

_____

_____

_____

_____

_____

_____

_____

_____

List the different colors of this tree in each season:

**Winter:** _____

**Spring:** _____

**Summer:** _____

**Autumn:** _____

How tall does this tree grow?

_____

What is the average diameter of the tree's trunk?

_____

What is the average lifespan of this tree?

_____

List the sources you used to research this tree:

Books: _____

_____

Websites: _____

Other sources: _____

_____

# IDAHO

The state tree is: **Western White Pine**

Find the botanical name: _____

List any other names by which this tree is known: _____

_____

Is this tree deciduous or coniferous (evergreen)? _____

Does this tree produce flowers? _____ Which season? _____

Does this tree produce fruit? _____ What kind? _____

Is this tree's trunk hardwood or softwood? _____

List some items made from the wood of this state tree: _____

_____

_____

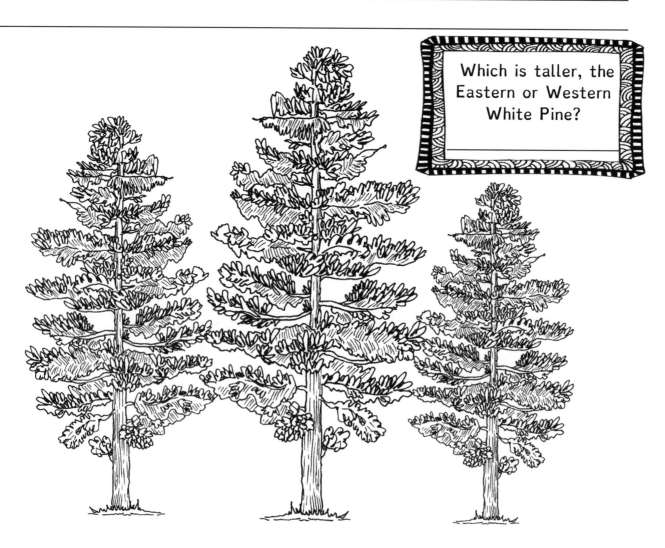

Which is taller, the Eastern or Western White Pine?

34

Find this state on page **5** and use a different color to fill it in.

What is the capital city of this state?

_____

# CREATIVE WRITING

In the space below, write a poem, short story, or a unique history tid-bit about the state tree. If this tree is in your state, and in season, try taping a leaf to this page and press it in the book!

_____

_____

_____

_____

_____

_____

_____

List the different colors of this tree in each season:

Winter: _____

Spring: _____

Summer: _____

Autumn: _____

How tall does this tree grow?

_____

What is the average diameter of the tree's trunk?

_____

What is the average lifespan of this tree?

_____

List the sources you used to research this tree:

Books: _____

Websites: _____

Other sources: _____

_____

# ILLINOIS

The state tree is: **White Oak**

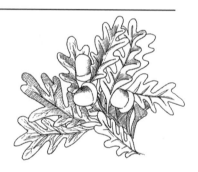

Find the botanical name: _____

    List any other names by which this tree is known: _____

_____

Is this tree deciduous or coniferous (evergreen)? _____

Does this tree produce flowers? _____ Which season? _____

    Does this tree produce fruit? _____ What kind? _____

Is this tree's trunk hardwood or softwood? _____

List some items made from the wood of this state tree: _____

_____

_____

Interesting fact:
White oak was used in the construction of *The USS Constitution* (also known as *Old Ironsides*), a wooden-hulled, three-masted heavy frigate of the U.S. Navy. Launched in 1797, she is the world's oldest commissioned naval vessel still afloat.

Find this state on page **5** and use a different color to fill it in.

What is the capital city of this state?
_____

# CREATIVE WRITING

In the space below, write a poem, short story, or a unique history tid-bit about the state tree. If this tree is in your state, and in season, try taping a leaf to this page and press it in the book!

_____
_____
_____
_____
_____
_____
_____

List the different colors of this tree in each season:

**Winter:** _____

**Spring:** _____

**Summer:** _____

**Autumn:** _____

How tall does this tree grow?
_____

What is the average diameter of the tree's trunk?
_____

What is the average lifespan of this tree?
_____

List the sources you used to research this tree:

Books: _____

Websites: _____

Other sources: _____

# INDIANA

The state tree is: **Tulip Poplar**

Find the botanical name: _____

List any other names by which this tree is known:

_____

Is this tree deciduous or coniferous (evergreen)? _____

Does this tree produce flowers? _____ Which season? _____

Does this tree produce fruit? _____ What kind? _____

Is this tree's trunk hardwood or softwood? _____

List some items made from the wood of this state tree: _____

_____

_____

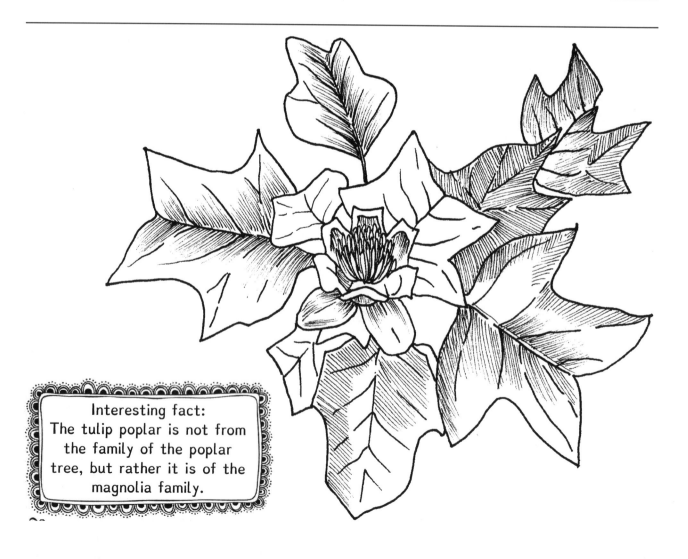

Interesting fact:
The tulip poplar is not from the family of the poplar tree, but rather it is of the magnolia family.

38

Find this state on page **5** and use a different color to fill it in.

What is the capital city of this state?
_____

# CREATIVE WRITING

In the space below, write a poem, short story, or a unique history tid-bit about the state tree. If this tree is in your state, and in season, try taping a leaf to this page and press it in the book!

_____
_____
_____
_____
_____
_____
_____

List the different colors of this tree in each season:

Winter: _____

Spring: _____

Summer: _____

Autumn: _____

How tall does this tree grow?
_____

What is the average diameter of the tree's trunk?
_____

What is the average lifespan of this tree?
_____

List the sources you used to research this tree:

Books: _____

Websites: _____

Other sources: _____

# IOWA

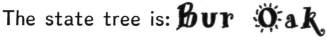

The state tree is: **Bur Oak**

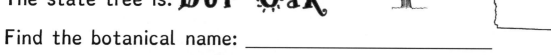

Find the botanical name: _____

   List any other names by which this tree is known: _____
_____

Is this tree deciduous or coniferous (evergreen)? _____

Does this tree produce flowers? _____ Which season? _____

   Does this tree produce fruit? _____ What kind? _____

Is this tree's trunk hardwood or softwood? _____

List some items made from the wood of this state tree: _____
_____
_____

Find this state on page **5** and use a different color to fill it in.

What is the capital city of this state?

_____

# CREATIVE WRITING

In the space below, write a poem, short story, or a unique history tid-bit about the state tree. If this tree is in your state, and in season, try taping a leaf to this page and press it in the book!

_____

_____

_____

_____

_____

_____

_____

_____

List the different colors of this tree in each season:

Winter: _____

Spring: _____

Summer: _____

Autumn: _____

How tall does this tree grow?

_____

What is the average diameter of the tree's trunk?

_____

What is the average lifespan of this tree?

_____

List the sources you used to research this tree:

Books: _____

_____

Websites: _____

Other sources: _____

# CREATIVE ARTS

Fill in the missing parts. Write the name of each tree from this section:

# CREATIVE ARTS

Draw your favorite tree from this section. Use your imagination to draw the tree in its natural habitat. Add a house, forest, or animals!

# KANSAS

The state tree is:
## Eastern Cottonwood

Find the botanical name: _____

List any other names by which this tree is known: _____

_____

Is this tree deciduous or coniferous (evergreen)? _____

Does this tree produce flowers? _____ Which season? _____

Does this tree produce fruit? _____ What kind? _____

Is this tree's trunk hardwood or softwood? _____

List some items made from the wood of this state tree: _____

_____

_____

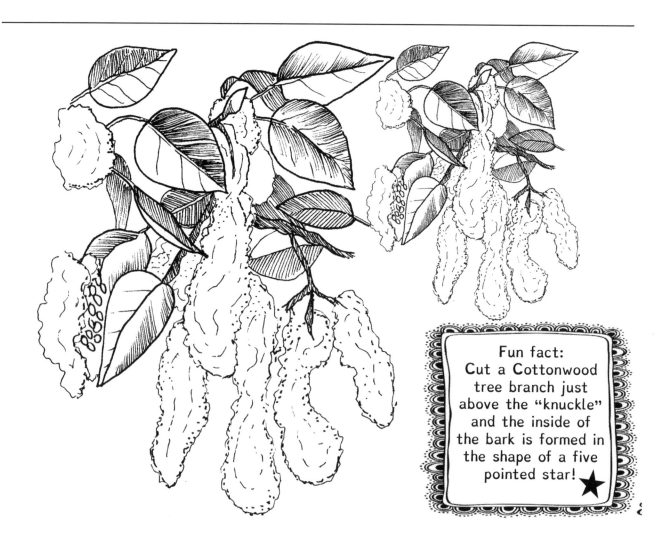

Fun fact:
Cut a Cottonwood tree branch just above the "knuckle" and the inside of the bark is formed in the shape of a five pointed star! ★

Find this state on page **5** and use a different color to fill it in.

What is the capital city of this state?
_____

# CREATIVE WRITING

In the space below, write a poem, short story, or a unique history tid-bit about the state tree. If this tree is in your state, and in season, try taping a leaf to this page and press it in the book!

_____
_____
_____
_____
_____
_____
_____

List the different colors of this tree in each season:

Winter: _____

Spring: _____

Summer: _____

Autumn: _____

How tall does this tree grow?
_____

What is the average diameter of the tree's trunk?
_____

What is the average lifespan of this tree?
_____

List the sources you used to research this tree:

Books: _____
_____

Websites: _____

Other sources: _____
_____

 # KENTUCKY

The state tree is: **Tulip Poplar**

Find the botanical name: _____

List any other names by which this tree is known: _____

_____

Is this tree deciduous or coniferous (evergreen)? _____

Does this tree produce flowers? _____ Which season? _____

Does this tree produce fruit? _____ What kind? _____

Is this tree's trunk hardwood or softwood? _____

List some items made from the wood of this state tree: _____

_____

Fun fact:
The tulip tree is also called the canoe tree because the Native Americans dug out the insides to make canoes.

Find this state on page **5** and use a different color to fill it in.

What is the capital city of this state?

_____

# CREATIVE WRITING

In the space below, write a poem, short story, or a unique history tid-bit about the state tree. If this tree is in your state, and in season, try taping a leaf to this page and press it in the book!

_____

_____

_____

_____

_____

_____

_____

_____

List the different colors of this tree in each season:

Winter: _____

Spring: _____

Summer: _____

Autumn: _____

How tall does this tree grow?

_____

What is the average diameter of the tree's trunk?

_____

What is the average lifespan of this tree?

_____

List the sources you used to research this tree:

Books: _____

_____

Websites: _____

_____

Other sources: _____

_____

# LOUISIANA

The state tree is: **Bald Cypress**

Find the botanical name: _____

    List any other names by which this tree is known: _____

_____

Is this tree deciduous or coniferous (evergreen)? _____

Does this tree produce flowers? _____ Which season? _____

    Does this tree produce fruit? _____ What kind? _____

Is this tree's trunk hardwood or softwood? _____

List some items made from the wood of this state tree: _____

_____

_____

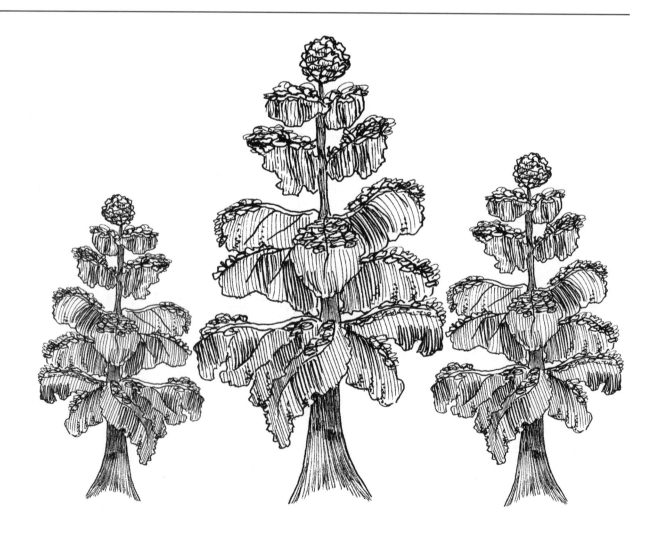

Find this state on page **5** and use a different color to fill it in.

What is the capital city of this state?
_____

# CREATIVE WRITING

In the space below, write a poem, short story, or a unique history tid-bit about the state tree. If this tree is in your state, and in season, try taping a leaf to this page and press it in the book!

_____
_____
_____
_____
_____
_____
_____
_____

List the different colors of this tree in each season:

**Winter:** _____

**Spring:** _____

**Summer:** _____

**Autumn:** _____

How tall does this tree grow?
_____

What is the average diameter of the tree's trunk?
_____

What is the average lifespan of this tree?
_____

List the sources you used to research this tree:

Books: _____
_____

Websites: _____
_____

Other sources: _____
_____

49

# MAINE

The state tree is: **White Pine**

Find the botanical name: _____

    List any other names by which this tree is known: _____

_____

Is this tree deciduous or coniferous (evergreen)? _____

Does this tree produce flowers? _____ Which season? _____

    Does this tree produce fruit? _____ What kind? _____

Is this tree's trunk hardwood or softwood? _____

List some items made from the wood of this state tree: _____

_____

_____

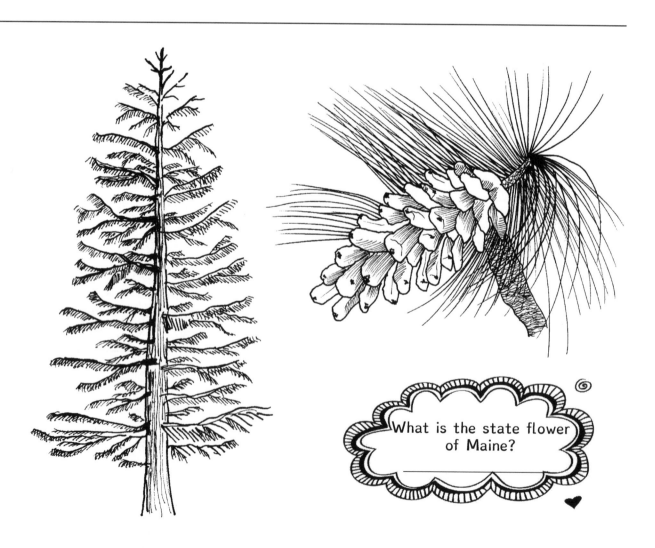

What is the state flower
of Maine?

_____

Find this state on page **5** and use a different color to fill it in.

What is the capital city of this state?
_____

# CREATIVE WRITING

In the space below, write a poem, short story, or a unique history tid-bit about the state tree. If this tree is in your state, and in season, try taping a leaf to this page and press it in the book!

_____
_____
_____
_____
_____
_____
_____
_____

List the different colors of this tree in each season:

Winter: _____

Spring: _____

Summer: _____

Autumn: _____

How tall does this tree grow?
_____

What is the average diameter of the tree's trunk?
_____

What is the average lifespan of this tree?
_____

List the sources you used to research this tree:

Books: _____

Websites: _____

Other sources: _____

# MARYLAND

The state tree is: **White Oak**

Find the botanical name: _____

   List any other names by which this tree is known: _____

_____

Is this tree deciduous or coniferous (evergreen)? _____

Does this tree produce flowers? _____ Which season? _____

   Does this tree produce fruit? _____ What kind? _____

Is this tree's trunk hardwood or softwood? _____

List some items made from the wood of this state tree: _____

_____

_____

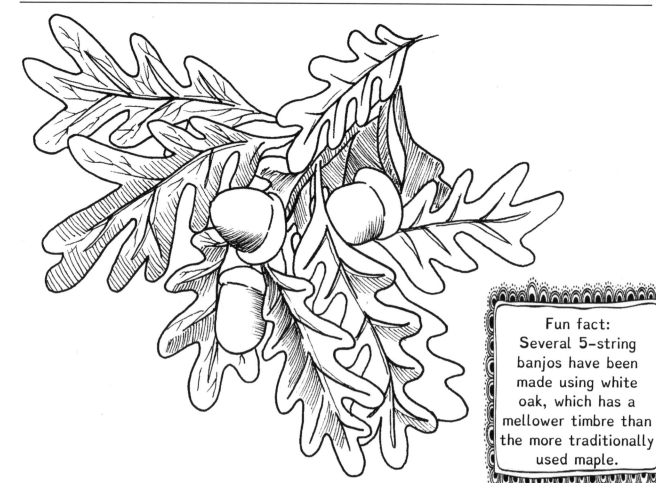

Fun fact:
Several 5-string banjos have been made using white oak, which has a mellower timbre than the more traditionally used maple.

Find this state on page **5** and use a different color to fill it in.

What is the capital city of this state?

_____

# CREATIVE WRITING

In the space below, write a poem, short story, or a unique history tid-bit about the state tree. If this tree is in your state, and in season, try taping a leaf to this page and press it in the book!

_____

_____

_____

_____

_____

_____

_____

_____

List the different colors of this tree in each season:

**Winter:** _____

**Spring:** _____

**Summer:** _____

**Autumn:** _____

How tall does this tree grow?

_____

What is the average diameter of the tree's trunk?

_____

What is the average lifespan of this tree?

_____

List the sources you used to research this tree:

**Books:** _____

**Websites:** _____

**Other sources:** _____

# CREATIVE ARTS

Fill in the missing parts. Write the name of each tree from this section:

# CREATIVE ARTS

Draw your favorite tree from this section. Use your imagination to draw the tree in its natural habitat. Add a house, forest, or animals!

# MASSACHUSETTS

The state tree is: American Elm

Find the botanical name: _____

List any other names by which this tree is known:
_____

Is this tree deciduous or coniferous (evergreen)? _____

Does this tree produce flowers? _____ Which season? _____

Does this tree produce fruit? _____ What kind? _____

Is this tree's trunk hardwood or softwood? _____

## The Elm Tree in History:

The Liberty Tree was a famous elm tree in Boston, Massachusetts, where the Patriots gathered to protest the oppressive rule of King George III of England, who imposed the Tea Act and the Stamp Act, leading to the Revolutionary War and the birth of the United States of America. In August 1775, the Liberty Tree was felled by Nathaniel Coffin Jr., a Loyalist to England. In 1776, the Patriots erected a Liberty Pole in its place, with several cities following suit.

Find this state on page **5** and use a different color to fill it in.

What is the capital city of this state?

_____

# CREATIVE WRITING

In the space below, write a poem, short story, or a unique history tid-bit about the state tree. If this tree is in your state, and in season, try taping a leaf to this page and press it in the book!

_____

_____

_____

_____

_____

_____

_____

List the different colors of this tree in each season:

**Winter:** _____

**Spring:** _____

**Summer:** _____

**Autumn:** _____

How tall does this tree grow?

_____

What is the average diameter of the tree's trunk?

_____

What is the average lifespan of this tree?

_____

List the sources you used to research this tree:

Books: _____

Websites: _____

Other sources: _____

# MICHIGAN

The state tree is: **Eastern White Pine**

Find the botanical name: _____

    List any other names by which this tree is known:

_____

Is this tree deciduous or coniferous (evergreen)? _____

Does this tree produce flowers? _____ Which season? _____

   Does this tree produce fruit? _____ What kind? _____

Is this tree's trunk hardwood or softwood? _____

List some items made from the wood of this state tree: _____

_____

_____

Find this state on page **5** and use a different color to fill it in.

What is the capital city of this state?

_____

## CREATIVE WRITING

In the space below, write a poem, short story, or a unique history tid-bit about the state tree. If this tree is in your state, and in season, try taping a leaf to this page and press it in the book!

_____

_____

_____

_____

_____

_____

_____

List the different colors of this tree in each season:

**Winter:** _____

**Spring:** _____

**Summer:** _____

**Autumn:** _____

How tall does this tree grow?

_____

What is the average diameter of the tree's trunk?

_____

What is the average lifespan of this tree?

_____

List the sources you used to research this tree:

Books: _____

_____

Websites: _____

Other sources: _____

_____

# MINNESOTA

The state tree is: **Red Pine**

Find the botanical name: _____

List any other names by which this tree is known: _____

_____

Is this tree deciduous or coniferous (evergreen)? _____

Does this tree produce flowers? _____ Which season? _____

Does this tree produce fruit? _____ What kind? _____

Is this tree's trunk hardwood or softwood? _____

List some items made from the wood of this state tree: _____

_____

_____

What is the difference between a red pine and a white

_____

_____

Find this state on page **5** and use a different color to fill it in.

What is the capital city of this state?
_____

## CREATIVE WRITING

In the space below, write a poem, short story, or a unique history tid-bit about the state tree. If this tree is in your state, and in season, try taping a leaf to this page and press it in the book!

_____
_____
_____
_____
_____
_____
_____
_____

List the different colors of this tree in each season:

Winter: _____

Spring: _____

Summer: _____

Autumn: _____

How tall does this tree grow?
_____

What is the average diameter of the tree's trunk?
_____

What is the average lifespan of this tree?

List the sources you used to research this tree:

Books: _____
_____

Websites: _____

Other sources: _____
_____

# MISSISSIPPI

The state tree is: **Magnolia**

Find the botanical name: _____

List any other names by which this tree is known: _____
_____

Is this tree deciduous or coniferous (evergreen)? _____

Does this tree produce flowers? _____ Which season? _____

Does this tree produce fruit? _____ What kind? _____

Is this tree's trunk hardwood or softwood? _____

List some items made from the wood of this state tree: _____
_____
_____

What is the state flower
of Mississippi?

Find this state on page **5** and use a different color to fill it in.

What is the capital city of this state?
_____

# CREATIVE WRITING

In the space below, write a poem, short story, or a unique history tid-bit about the state tree. If this tree is in your state, and in season, try taping a leaf to this page and press it in the book!

_____
_____
_____
_____
_____
_____
_____

List the different colors of this tree in each season:

Winter: _____

Spring: _____

Summer: _____

Autumn: _____

How tall does this tree grow?
_____

What is the average diameter of the tree's trunk?
_____

What is the average lifespan of this tree?
_____

List the sources you used to research this tree:

Books: _____
_____

Websites: _____

Other sources: _____

# MISSOURI

The state tree is: **Flowering Dogwood**

Find the botanical name: _____

List any other names by which this tree is known: _____

_____

Is this tree deciduous or coniferous (evergreen)? _____

Does this tree produce flowers? _____ Which season? _____

Does this tree produce fruit? _____ What kind? _____

Is this tree's trunk hardwood or softwood? _____

List some items made from the wood of this state tree: _____

_____

_____

Interesting tid-bit:
The dogwood tree is the
subject of a famous poem
by an unknown author: The
Legend of the Dogwood

Find this state on page **5** and use a different color to fill it in.

What is the capital city of this state?
_____

# CREATIVE WRITING

In the space below, write a poem, short story, or a unique history tid-bit about the state tree. If this tree is in your state, and in season, try taping a leaf to this page and press it in the book!

_____
_____
_____
_____
_____
_____
_____
_____

List the different colors of this tree in each season:

**Winter:** _____

**Spring:** _____

**Summer:** _____

**Autumn:** _____

How tall does this tree grow?
_____

What is the average diameter of the tree's trunk?
_____

What is the average lifespan of this tree?
_____

List the sources you used to research this tree:

Books: _____

Websites: _____

Other sources: _____

# CREATIVE ARTS

Fill in the missing parts. Write the name of each tree from this section:

# CREATIVE ARTS

Draw your favorite tree from this section. Use your imagination to draw the tree in its natural habitat. Add a house, forest, or animals!

# MONTANA

The state tree is: **Ponderosa Pine**

Find the botanical name: _____

    List any other names by which this tree is known: _____
_____

Is this tree deciduous or coniferous (evergreen)? _____

Does this tree produce flowers? _____ Which season? _____

    Does this tree produce fruit? _____ What kind? _____

Is this tree's trunk hardwood or softwood? _____

List some items made from the wood of this state tree: _____
_____
_____

Fun fact:
Ponderosa needles are
the only known food for
the caterpillars of the
twirler moth.

Draw a twirler moth:

Find this state on page **5** and use a different color to fill it in.

What is the capital city of this state?

_____

# CREATIVE WRITING

In the space below, write a poem, short story, or a unique history tid-bit about the state tree. If this tree is in your state, and in season, try taping a leaf to this page and press it in the book!

_____

_____

_____

_____

_____

_____

_____

_____

List the different colors of this tree in each season:

Winter: _____

Spring: _____

Summer: _____

Autumn: _____

How tall does this tree grow?
_____

What is the average diameter of the tree's trunk?
_____

What is the average lifespan of this tree?
_____

List the sources you used to research this tree:

Books: _____

Websites: _____

Other sources: _____

# NEBRASKA

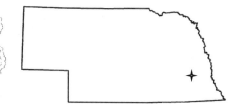

The state tree is:

## Eastern Cottonwood

Find the botanical name: _____

List any other names by which this tree is known: _____

_____

Is this tree deciduous or coniferous (evergreen)? _____

Does this tree produce flowers? _____ Which season? _____

Does this tree produce fruit? _____ What kind? _____

Is this tree's trunk hardwood or softwood? _____

List some items made from the wood of this state tree: _____

_____

_____

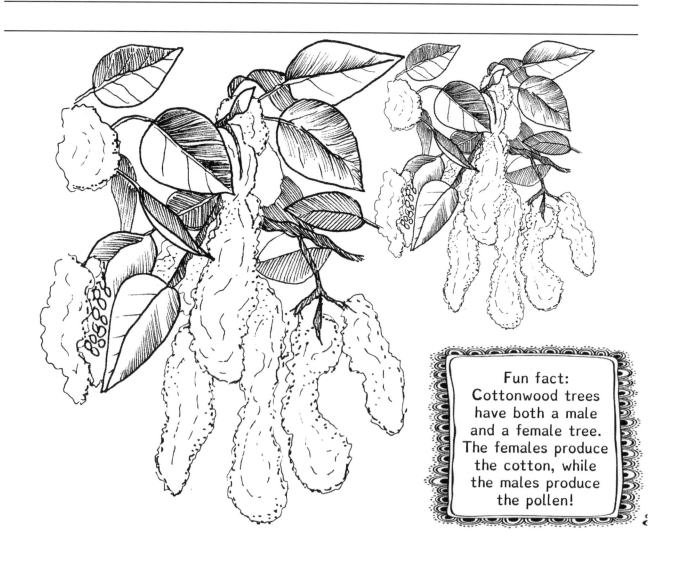

Fun fact:
Cottonwood trees
have both a male
and a female tree.
The females produce
the cotton, while
the males produce
the pollen!

Find this state on page **5** and use a different color to fill it in.

What is the capital city of this state?

_____

# CREATIVE WRITING

In the space below, write a poem, short story, or a unique history tid-bit about the state tree. If this tree is in your state, and in season, try taping a leaf to this page and press it in the book!

_____

_____

_____

_____

_____

_____

List the different colors of this tree in each season:

**Winter:** _____

**Spring:** _____

**Summer:** _____

**Autumn:** _____

How tall does this tree grow?

_____

What is the average diameter of the tree's trunk?

_____

What is the average lifespan of this tree?

_____

List the sources you used to research this tree:

Books: _____

Websites: _____

Other sources: _____

_____

# NEVADA

The state tree is:

## Single-Leaf Piñon Pine

Find the botanical name: _____

List any other names by which this tree is known: _____

_____

Is this tree deciduous or coniferous (evergreen)? _____

Does this tree produce flowers? _____ Which season? _____

Does this tree produce fruit? _____ What kind? _____

Is this tree's trunk hardwood or softwood? _____

List some items made from the wood of this state tree: _____

_____

Interesting fact:
The single-leaf piñon
pine is the world's only
one-needled pine tree

Find this state on page **5** and use a different color to fill it in.

What is the capital city of this state?
_____

# CREATIVE WRITING

In the space below, write a poem, short story, or a unique history tid-bit about the state tree. If this tree is in your state, and in season, try taping a leaf to this page and press it in the book!

_____
_____
_____
_____
_____
_____
_____
_____

List the different colors of this tree in each season:

**Winter:** _____

**Spring:** _____

**Summer:** _____

**Autumn:** _____

How tall does this tree grow?
_____

What is the average diameter of the tree's trunk?
_____

What is the average lifespan of this tree?
_____

List the sources you used to research this tree:

**Books:** _____
_____

**Websites:** _____
_____

**Other sources:** _____
_____

# NEW HAMPSHIRE

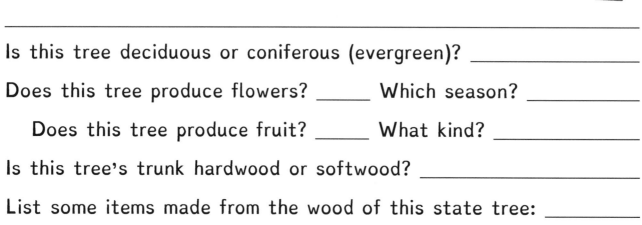

The state tree is: American White Birch

Find the botanical name: _____

  List any other names by which this tree is known:

_____

Is this tree deciduous or coniferous (evergreen)? _____

Does this tree produce flowers? _____ Which season? _____

  Does this tree produce fruit? _____ What kind? _____

Is this tree's trunk hardwood or softwood? _____

List some items made from the wood of this state tree: _____

_____

_____

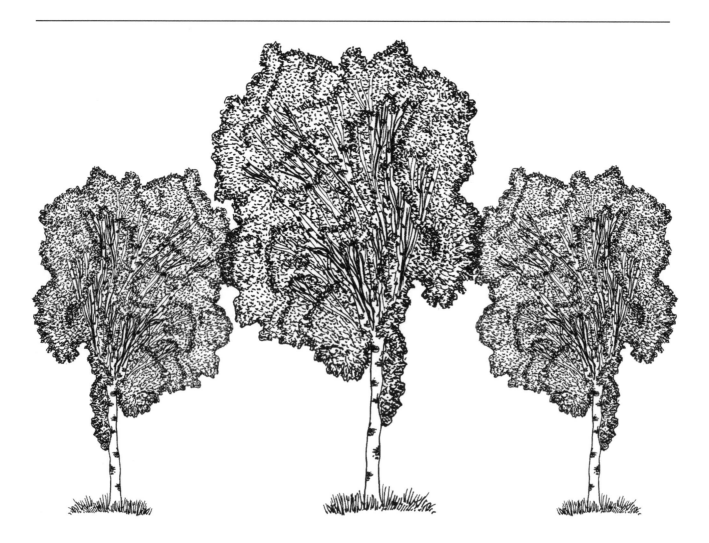

Find this state on page **5** and use a different color to fill it in.

What is the capital city of this state?

_____

# CREATIVE WRITING

In the space below, write a poem, short story, or a unique history tid-bit about the state tree. If this tree is in your state, and in season, try taping a leaf to this page and press it in the book!

_____

_____

_____

_____

_____

_____

_____

List the different colors of this tree in each season:

Winter: _____

Spring: _____

Summer: _____

Autumn: _____

How tall does this tree grow?

_____

What is the average diameter of the tree's trunk?

_____

What is the average lifespan of this tree?

_____

List the sources you used to research this tree:

Books: _____

_____

Websites: _____

Other sources: _____

_____

# NEW JERSEY

The state tree is: Northern Red Oak

Find the botanical name: _____

List any other names by which this tree is known:

_____

Is this tree deciduous or coniferous (evergreen)? _____

Does this tree produce flowers? _____ Which season? _____

Does this tree produce fruit? _____ What kind? _____

Is this tree's trunk hardwood or softwood? _____

List some items made from the wood of this state tree: _____

_____

_____

List the 6 states that declared a variety of Oak for their state tree:

_____
_____
_____
_____
_____
_____

Find this state on page 5 and use a different color to fill it in.

What is the capital city of this state?

_____

## CREATIVE WRITING

In the space below, write a poem, short story, or a unique history tid-bit about the state tree. If this tree is in your state, and in season, try taping a leaf to this page and press it in the book!

_____

_____

_____

_____

_____

_____

_____

List the different colors of this tree in each season:

**Winter:** _____

**Spring:** _____

**Summer:** _____

**Autumn:** _____

How tall does this tree grow?

_____

What is the average diameter of the tree's trunk?

_____

What is the average lifespan of this tree?

_____

List the sources you used to research this tree:

**Books:** _____

**Websites:** _____

**Other sources:** _____

# CREATIVE ARTS

Fill in the missing parts. Write the name of each tree from this section:

# CREATIVE ARTS

Draw your favorite tree from this section. Use your imagination to draw the tree in its natural habitat. Add a house, forest, or animals!

# NEW MEXICO

The state tree is:
## Two-needle Piñon Pine

Find the botanical name: _____

List any other names by which this tree is known: _____

_____

Is this tree deciduous or coniferous (evergreen)? _____

Does this tree produce flowers? _____ Which season? _____

Does this tree produce fruit? _____ What kind? _____

Is this tree's trunk hardwood or softwood? _____

List some items made from the wood of this state tree: _____

_____

Fun fact:
The Piñon Pine is used
for the Christmas tree
in the southwest
states.

Find this state on page **5** and use a different color to fill it in.

What is the capital city of this state?
_____

# CREATIVE WRITING

In the space below, write a poem, short story, or a unique history tid-bit about the state tree. If this tree is in your state, and in season, try taping a leaf to this page and press it in the book!

_____
_____
_____
_____
_____
_____
_____

List the different colors of this tree in each season:

Winter: _____

Spring: _____

Summer: _____

Autumn: _____

How tall does this tree grow?
_____

What is the average diameter of the tree's trunk?
_____

What is the average lifespan of this tree?
_____

List the sources you used to research this tree:

Books: _____

Websites: _____

Other sources: _____

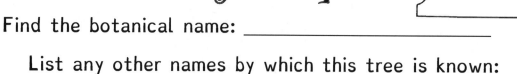

# NEW YORK

The state tree is: Sugar Maple

Find the botanical name: _____

List any other names by which this tree is known:

_____

Is this tree deciduous or coniferous (evergreen)? _____

Does this tree produce flowers? _____ Which season? _____

Does this tree produce fruit? _____ What kind? _____

Is this tree's trunk hardwood or softwood? _____

List some items made from the wood of this state tree: _____

_____

_____

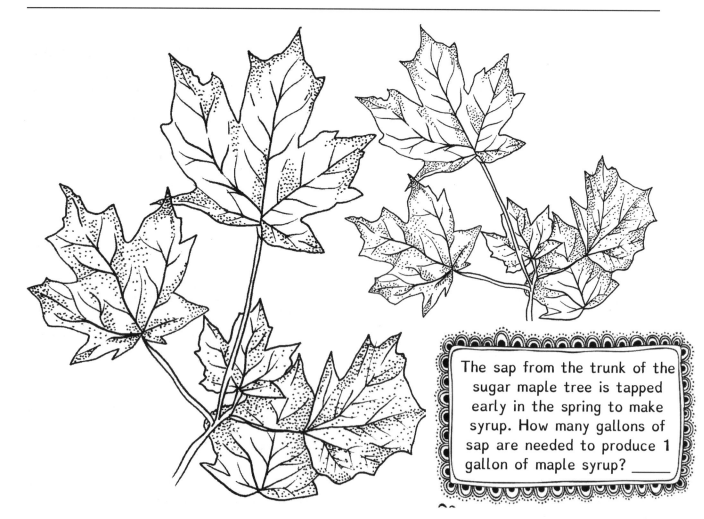

The sap from the trunk of the sugar maple tree is tapped early in the spring to make syrup. How many gallons of sap are needed to produce **1** gallon of maple syrup? _____

Find this state on page **5** and use a different color to fill it in.

What is the capital city of this state?

_____

# CREATIVE WRITING

In the space below, write a poem, short story, or a unique history tid-bit about the state tree. If this tree is in your state, and in season, try taping a leaf to this page and press it in the book!

_____

_____

_____

_____

_____

_____

_____

_____

**List the different colors of this tree in each season:**

**Winter:** _____

**Spring:** _____

**Summer:** _____

**Autumn:** _____

**How tall does this tree grow?**

_____

**What is the average diameter of the tree's trunk?**

_____

**What is the average lifespan of this tree?**

_____

**List the sources you used to research this tree:**

Books: _____

Websites: _____

Other sources: _____

_____

# NORTH CAROLINA

The state tree is: **Pine Tree**

Find the botanical name: _____

List any other names by which this tree is known: _____
_____

Is this tree deciduous or coniferous (evergreen)? _____

Does this tree produce flowers? _____ Which season? _____

Does this tree produce fruit? _____ What kind? _____

Is this tree's trunk hardwood or softwood? _____

List some items made from the wood of this state tree: _____
_____
_____

List the 9 states
that declared a
variety of Pine
for their state tree:

_____
_____
_____
_____
_____
_____
_____
_____
_____

Find this state on page **5** and use a different color to fill it in.

What is the capital city of this state?

_____

## ✴ CREATIVE WRITING ✴

In the space below, write a poem, short story, or a unique history tid-bit about the state tree. If this tree is in your state, and in season, try taping a leaf to this page and press it in the book!

_____

_____

_____

_____

_____

_____

_____

List the different colors of this tree in each season:

**Winter:** _____

**Spring:** _____

**Summer:** _____

**Autumn:** _____

How tall does this tree grow?

_____

What is the average diameter of the tree's trunk?

_____

What is the average lifespan of this tree?

_____

List the sources you used to research this tree:

**Books:** _____

_____

**Websites:** _____

_____

**Other sources:** _____

_____

# NORTH DAKOTA

The state tree is: **American Elm**

Find the botanical name: _____

List any other names by which this tree is known: _____
_____

Is this tree deciduous or coniferous (evergreen)? _____

Does this tree produce flowers? _____ Which season? _____

Does this tree produce fruit? _____ What kind? _____

Is this tree's trunk hardwood or softwood? _____

List some items made from the wood of this state tree: _____
_____
_____

Which other state declared American Elm as their state tree?
_____

86

Find this state on page **5** and use a different color to fill it in.

What is the capital city of this state?

_____

# CREATIVE WRITING

In the space below, write a poem, short story, or a unique history tid-bit about the state tree. If this tree is in your state, and in season, try taping a leaf to this page and press it in the book!

_____

_____

_____

_____

_____

_____

_____

List the different colors of this tree in each season:

**Winter:** _____

**Spring:** _____

**Summer:** _____

**Autumn:** _____

How tall does this tree grow?

_____

What is the average diameter of the tree's trunk?

_____

What is the average lifespan of this tree?

_____

List the sources you used to research this tree:

Books: _____

Websites: _____

Other sources: _____

# OHIO

The state tree is: **Buckeye**

Find the botanical name: _____

    List any other names by which this tree is known:

_____

Is this tree deciduous or coniferous (evergreen)? _____

Does this tree produce flowers? _____ Which season? _____

   Does this tree produce fruit? _____ What kind? _____

Is this tree's trunk hardwood or softwood? _____

List some items made from the wood of this state tree: _____

_____

_____

Find this state on page **5** and use a different color to fill it in.

What is the capital city of this state?

_____

## CREATIVE WRITING

In the space below, write a poem, short story, or a unique history tid-bit about the state tree. If this tree is in your state, and in season, try taping a leaf to this page and press it in the book!

_____

_____

_____

_____

_____

_____

_____

_____

List the different colors of this tree in each season:

**Winter:** _____

**Spring:** _____

**Summer:** _____

**Autumn:** _____

How tall does this tree grow?

_____

What is the average diameter of the tree's trunk?

_____

What is the average lifespan of this tree?

_____

List the sources you used to research this tree:

**Books:** _____

**Websites:** _____

**Other sources:** _____

# CREATIVE ARTS

Fill in the missing parts. Write the name of each tree from this section:

# CREATIVE ARTS

Draw your favorite tree from this section. Use your imagination to draw the tree in its natural habitat. Add a house, forest, or animals!

# OKLAHOMA

The state tree is: **Eastern Redbud**

Find the botanical name: _____

   List any other names by which this tree is known: _____

_____

Is this tree deciduous or coniferous (evergreen)? _____

Does this tree produce flowers? _____ Which season? _____

   Does this tree produce fruit? _____ What kind? _____

Is this tree's trunk hardwood or softwood? _____

List some items made from the wood of this state tree: _____

_____

_____

Fun fact:
Redbud flowers are edible! Add redbuds to your salad or try making Redbud Jelly!

Find this state on page **5** and use a different color to fill it in.

What is the capital city of this state?

_____

# CREATIVE WRITING

In the space below, write a poem, short story, or a unique history tid-bit about the state tree. If this tree is in your state, and in season, try taping a leaf to this page and press it in the book!

_____

_____

_____

_____

_____

_____

_____

List the different colors of this tree in each season:

**Winter:** _____

**Spring:** _____

**Summer:** _____

**Autumn:** _____

How tall does this tree grow?

_____

What is the average diameter of the tree's trunk?

_____

What is the average lifespan of this tree?

_____

List the sources you used to research this tree:

Books: _____

Websites: _____

Other sources: _____

# OREGON

The state tree is: *Douglas Fir*

Find the botanical name: _____

   List any other names by which this tree is known: _____

_____

Is this tree deciduous or coniferous (evergreen)? _____

Does this tree produce flowers? _____ Which season? _____

   Does this tree produce fruit? _____ What kind? _____

Is this tree's trunk hardwood or softwood? _____

List some items made from the wood of this state tree: _____

_____

_____

Fun fact:
The Douglas-fir was used for three masts on the restored **USS Constitution** (also known as *Old Ironsides*), a wooden-hulled, three-masted heavy frigate of the **U.S. Navy** originally launched in **1797**.

94

Find this state on page **5** and use a different color to fill it in.

What is the capital city of this state?

_____

# CREATIVE WRITING

In the space below, write a poem, short story, or a unique history tid-bit about the state tree. If this tree is in your state, and in season, try taping a leaf to this page and press it in the book!

_____

_____

_____

_____

_____

_____

_____

_____

_____

**List the different colors of this tree in each season:**

**Winter:** _____

**Spring:** _____

**Summer:** _____

**Autumn:** _____

**How tall does this tree grow?**
_____

**What is the average diameter of the tree's trunk?**
_____

**What is the average lifespan of this tree?**
_____

**List the sources you used to research this tree:**

Books: _____

_____

Websites: _____

Other sources: _____

_____

# PENNSYLVANIA

The state tree is: **Eastern Hemlock**

Find the botanical name: _____

List any other names by which this tree is known: _____

_____

Is this tree deciduous or coniferous (evergreen)? _____

Does this tree produce flowers? _____ Which season? _____

Does this tree produce fruit? _____ What kind? _____

Is this tree's trunk hardwood or softwood? _____

List some items made from the wood of this state tree: _____

_____

_____

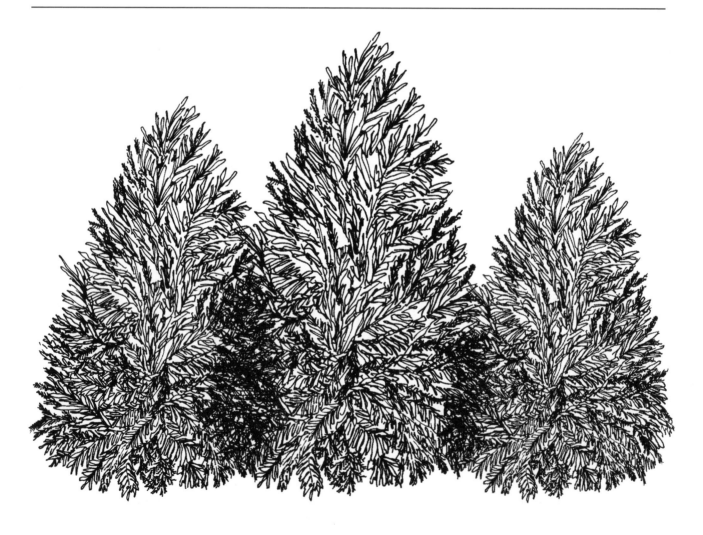

Find this state on page **5** and use a different color to fill it in.

What is the capital city of this state?

_____

# CREATIVE WRITING

In the space below, write a poem, short story, or a unique history tid-bit about the state tree. If this tree is in your state, and in season, try taping a leaf to this page and press it in the book!

_____

_____

_____

_____

_____

_____

_____

_____

List the different colors of this tree in each season:

**Winter:** _____

**Spring:** _____

**Summer:** _____

**Autumn:** _____

How tall does this tree grow?

_____

What is the average diameter of the tree's trunk?

_____

What is the average lifespan of this tree?

_____

List the sources you used to research this tree:

**Books:** _____

**Websites:** _____

**Other sources:** _____

# RHODE ISLAND

The state tree is: Red Maple

Find the botanical name: _____

List any other names by which this tree is known: 

_____

Is this tree deciduous or coniferous (evergreen)? _____

Does this tree produce flowers? _____ Which season? _____

Does this tree produce fruit? _____ What kind? _____

Is this tree's trunk hardwood or softwood? _____

List some items made from the wood of this state tree: _____

_____

_____

Find this state on page **5** and use a different color to fill it in.

What is the capital city of this state?

_____

# CREATIVE WRITING

In the space below, write a poem, short story, or a unique history tid-bit about the state tree. If this tree is in your state, and in season, try taping a leaf to this page and press it in the book!

_____

_____

_____

_____

_____

_____

_____

List the different colors of this tree in each season:

**Winter:** _____

**Spring:** _____

**Summer:** _____

**Autumn:** _____

How tall does this tree grow?

_____

What is the average diameter of the tree's trunk?

_____

What is the average lifespan of this tree?

List the sources you used to research this tree:

**Books:** _____

**Websites:** _____

**Other sources:** _____

_____

# SOUTH CAROLINA

The state tree is: Sable Palm

Find the botanical name: _____

List any other names by which this tree is known:

_____

Is this tree deciduous or coniferous (evergreen)? _____

Does this tree produce flowers? _____ Which season? _____

Does this tree produce fruit? _____ What kind? _____

Is this tree's trunk hardwood or softwood? _____

List some items made from the wood of this state tree: _____

_____

_____

Which other state declared Sable Palm as their state tree?

_____

Find this state on page **5** and use a different color to fill it in.

What is the capital city of this state?

_____

# CREATIVE WRITING

In the space below, write a poem, short story, or a unique history tid-bit about the state tree. If this tree is in your state, and in season, try taping a leaf to this page and press it in the book!

_____

_____

_____

_____

_____

_____

_____

**List the different colors of this tree in each season:**

Winter: _____

Spring: _____

Summer: _____

Autumn: _____

How tall does this tree grow?

_____

What is the average diameter of the tree's trunk?

_____

What is the average lifespan of this tree?

_____

**List the sources you used to research this tree:**

Books: _____

Websites: _____

Other sources: _____

_____

# CREATIVE ARTS

Fill in the missing parts. Write the name of each tree from this section:

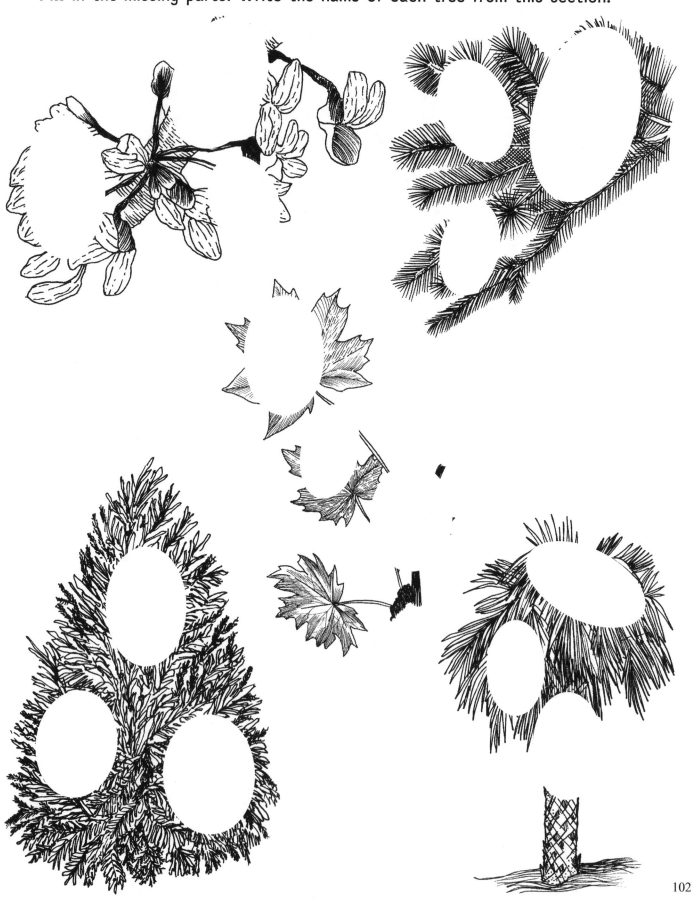

# CREATIVE ARTS

Draw your favorite tree from this section. Use your imagination to draw the tree in its natural habitat. Add a house, forest, or animals!

# SOUTH DAKOTA

The state tree is:

## Black Hills Spruce

Find the botanical name: _____

List any other names by which this tree is known: _____

_____

Is this tree deciduous or coniferous (evergreen)? _____

Does this tree produce flowers? _____ Which season? _____

Does this tree produce fruit? _____ What kind? _____

Is this tree's trunk hardwood or softwood? _____

List some items made from the wood of this state tree: _____

_____

_____

Three states picked a variety of Spruce for their state tree. Name the other two states:

_____

_____

Find this state on page **5** and use a different color to fill it in.

What is the capital city of this state?

_____

# CREATIVE WRITING

In the space below, write a poem, short story, or a unique history tid-bit about the state tree. If this tree is in your state, and in season, try taping a leaf to this page and press it in the book!

_____

_____

_____

_____

_____

_____

_____

List the different colors of this tree in each season:

Winter: _____

Spring: _____

Summer: _____

Autumn: _____

How tall does this tree grow?

_____

What is the average diameter of the tree's trunk?

_____

What is the average lifespan of this tree?

_____

List the sources you used to research this tree:

Books: _____

_____

Websites: _____

_____

Other sources: _____

_____

# TENNESSEE

The state tree is:

## Tulip Poplar

Find the botanical name: _____

List any other names by which this tree is known: _____

_____

Is this tree deciduous or coniferous (evergreen)? _____

Does this tree produce flowers? _____ Which season? _____

Does this tree produce fruit? _____ What kind? _____

Is this tree's trunk hardwood or softwood? _____

List some items made from the wood of this state tree: _____

_____

_____

Which three states declared the tulip for their state tree?

_____

_____

_____

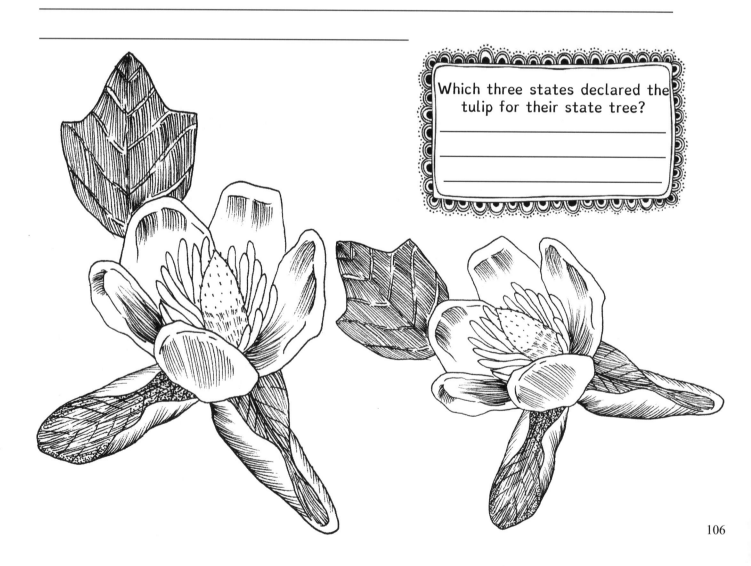

106

Find this state on page **5** and use a different color to fill it in.

What is the capital city of this state?

_____

# CREATIVE WRITING

In the space below, write a poem, short story, or a unique history tid-bit about the state tree. If this tree is in your state, and in season, try taping a leaf to this page and press it in the book!

_____

_____

_____

_____

_____

_____

_____

List the different colors of this tree in each season:

**Winter:** _____

**Spring:** _____

**Summer:** _____

**Autumn:** _____

How tall does this tree grow?

_____

What is the average diameter of the tree's trunk?

_____

What is the average lifespan of this tree?

_____

List the sources you used to research this tree:

**Books:** _____

**Websites:** _____

**Other sources:** _____

# TEXAS

The state tree is: **Pecan**

Find the botanical name: _____

   List any other names by which this tree is known:

_____

Is this tree deciduous or coniferous (evergreen)? _____

Does this tree produce flowers? _____ Which season? _____

   Does this tree produce fruit? _____ What kind? _____

Is this tree's trunk hardwood or softwood? _____

List some items made from the wood of this state tree: _____

_____

_____

Find this state on page **5** and use a different color to fill it in.

What is the capital city of this state?
_____

# CREATIVE WRITING

In the space below, write a poem, short story, or a unique history tid-bit about the state tree. If this tree is in your state, and in season, try taping a leaf to this page and press it in the book!

_____
_____
_____
_____
_____
_____
_____

List the different colors of this tree in each season:

**Winter:** _____

**Spring:** _____

**Summer:** _____

**Autumn:** _____

How tall does this tree grow?
_____

What is the average diameter of the tree's trunk?
_____

What is the average lifespan of this tree?
_____

List the sources you used to research this tree:

**Books:** _____
_____

**Websites:** _____
_____

**Other sources:** _____
_____

# UTAH

The state tree is: **Quaking Aspen**

Find the botanical name: _____

List any other names by which this tree is known:

_____

Is this tree deciduous or coniferous (evergreen)? _____

Does this tree produce flowers? _____ Which season? _____

Does this tree produce fruit? _____ What kind? _____

Is this tree's trunk hardwood or softwood? _____

List some items made from the wood of this state tree: _____

_____

_____

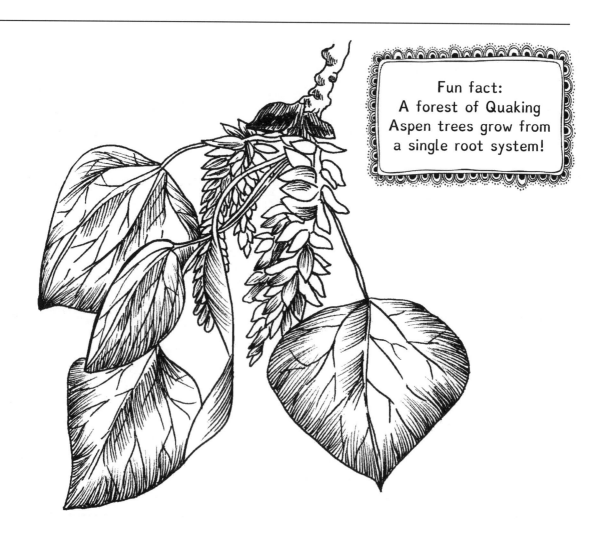

Fun fact:
A forest of Quaking Aspen trees grow from a single root system!

Find this state on page **5** and use a different color to fill it in.

What is the capital city of this state?

_____

## CREATIVE WRITING

In the space below, write a poem, short story, or a unique history tid-bit about the state tree. If this tree is in your state, and in season, try taping a leaf to this page and press it in the book!

_____

_____

_____

_____

_____

_____

_____

List the different colors of this tree in each season:

**Winter:** _____

**Spring:** _____

**Summer:** _____

**Autumn:** _____

How tall does this tree grow?

_____

What is the average diameter of the tree's trunk?

_____

What is the average lifespan of this tree?

_____

List the sources you used to research this tree:

**Books:** _____

_____

**Websites:** _____

_____

**Other sources:** _____

_____

# VERMONT

The state tree is: **Sugar Maple**

Find the botanical name: _____

List any other names by which this tree is known:

_____

Is this tree deciduous or coniferous (evergreen)? _____

Does this tree produce flowers? _____ Which season? _____

Does this tree produce fruit? _____ What kind? _____

Is this tree's trunk hardwood or softwood? _____

List some items made from the wood of this state tree: _____

_____

_____

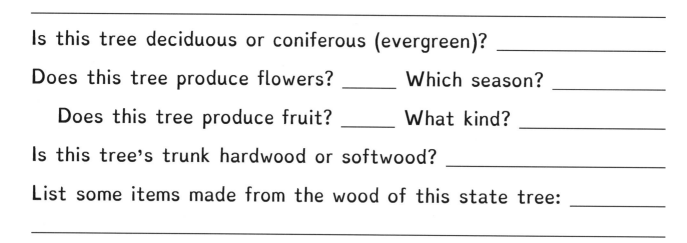

What is the difference between a Red Maple and a Sugar Maple?

_____

_____

_____

112

Find this state on page **5** and use a different color to fill it in.

What is the capital city of this state?

_____

## ✳ CREATIVE WRITING ✳

In the space below, write a poem, short story, or a unique history tid-bit about the state tree. If this tree is in your state, and in season, try taping a leaf to this page and press it in the book!

_____

_____

_____

_____

_____

_____

_____

List the different colors of this tree in each season:

**Winter:** _____

**Spring:** _____

**Summer:** _____

**Autumn:** _____

How tall does this tree grow?

_____

What is the average diameter of the tree's trunk?

_____

What is the average lifespan of this tree?

_____

List the sources you used to research this tree:

**Books:** _____

_____

**Websites:** _____

_____

**Other sources:** _____

_____

# CREATIVE ARTS

Fill in the missing parts. Write the name of each tree from this section:

# CREATIVE ARTS

Draw your favorite tree from this section. Use your imagination to draw the tree in its natural habitat. Add a house, forest, or animals!

# VIRGINIA

The state tree is:
## Flowering Dogwood

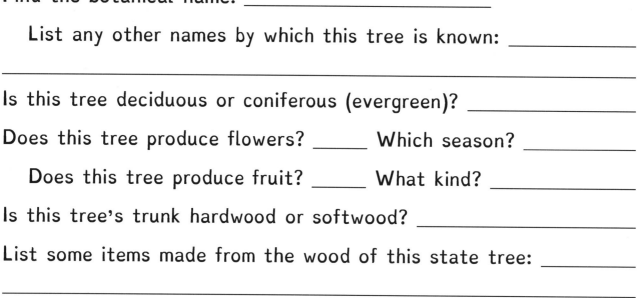

Find the botanical name: _____

List any other names by which this tree is known: _____

_____

Is this tree deciduous or coniferous (evergreen)? _____

Does this tree produce flowers? _____ Which season? _____

Does this tree produce fruit? _____ What kind? _____

Is this tree's trunk hardwood or softwood? _____

List some items made from the wood of this state tree: _____

_____

_____

Which other state declared the Dogwood for their state tree?

What is the state flower of Virginia?

Find this state on page **5** and use a different color to fill it in.

What is the capital city of this state?

_____

# CREATIVE WRITING

In the space below, write a poem, short story, or a unique history tid-bit about the state tree. If this tree is in your state, and in season, try taping a leaf to this page and press it in the book!

_____

_____

_____

_____

_____

_____

_____

List the different colors of this tree in each season:

**Winter:** _____

**Spring:** _____

**Summer:** _____

**Autumn:** _____

How tall does this tree grow?

_____

What is the average diameter of the tree's trunk?

_____

What is the average lifespan of this tree?

_____

List the sources you used to research this tree:

Books: _____

Websites: _____

Other sources: _____

# WASHINGTON

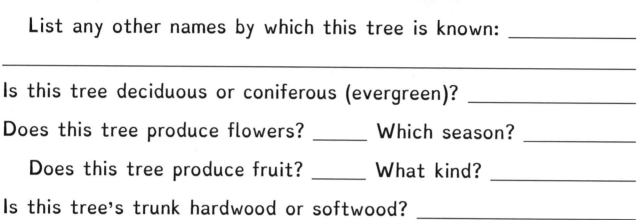

The state flower is:

## Western Hemlock

Find the botanical name: _____

List any other names by which this tree is known: _____
_____

Is this tree deciduous or coniferous (evergreen)? _____

Does this tree produce flowers? _____ Which season? _____

Does this tree produce fruit? _____ What kind? _____

Is this tree's trunk hardwood or softwood? _____

List some items made from the wood of this state tree: _____
_____
_____

One other state declared a Hemlock for their state tree. Name the other state:
_____

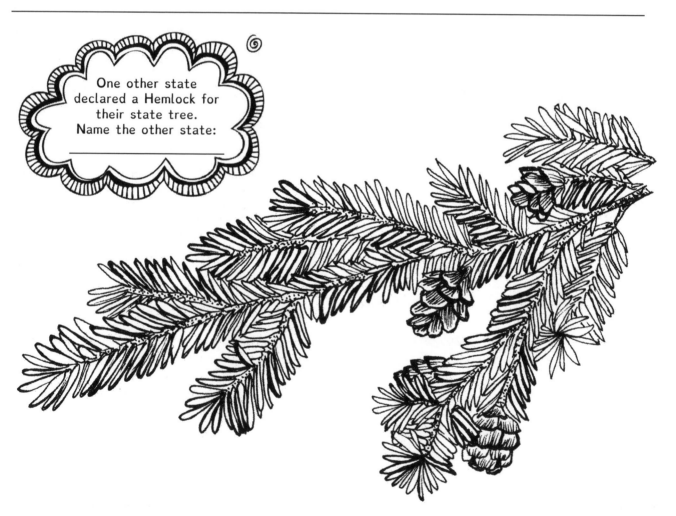

118

Find this state on page **5** and use a different color to fill it in.

What is the capital city of this state?

_____

# CREATIVE WRITING

In the space below, write a poem, short story, or a unique history tid-bit about the state tree. If this tree is in your state, and in season, try taping a leaf to this page and press it in the book!

_____

_____

_____

_____

_____

_____

_____

List the different colors of this tree in each season:

Winter: _____

Spring: _____

Summer: _____

Autumn: _____

How tall does this tree grow?

_____

What is the average diameter of the tree's trunk?

_____

What is the average lifespan of this tree?

_____

List the sources you used to research this tree:

Books: _____

Websites: _____

Other sources: _____

# WEST VIRGINIA

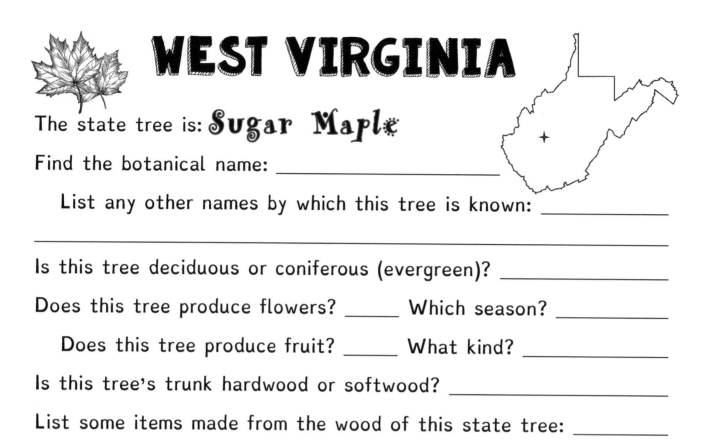

The state tree is: Sugar Maple

Find the botanical name: _____

List any other names by which this tree is known: _____

_____

Is this tree deciduous or coniferous (evergreen)? _____

Does this tree produce flowers? _____ Which season? _____

Does this tree produce fruit? _____ What kind? _____

Is this tree's trunk hardwood or softwood? _____

List some items made from the wood of this state tree: _____

_____

_____

120

Find this state on page **5** and use a different color to fill it in.

What is the capital city of this state?

_____

# CREATIVE WRITING

In the space below, write a poem, short story, or a unique history tid-bit about the state tree. If this tree is in your state, and in season, try taping a leaf to this page and press it in the book!

_____

_____

_____

_____

_____

_____

_____

_____

List the different colors of this tree in each season:

**Winter:** _____

**Spring:** _____

**Summer:** _____

**Autumn:** _____

How tall does this tree grow?

_____

What is the average diameter of the tree's trunk?

_____

What is the average lifespan of this tree?

_____

List the sources you used to research this tree:

**Books:** _____

_____

**Websites:** _____

_____

**Other sources:** _____

_____

# WISCONSIN

The state tree is: **Sugar Maple**

Find the botanical name: _____

    List any other names by which this tree is known: _____

_____

Is this tree deciduous or coniferous (evergreen)? _____

Does this tree produce flowers? _____ Which season? _____

    Does this tree produce fruit? _____ What kind? _____

Is this tree's trunk hardwood or softwood? _____

List some items made from the wood of this state tree: _____

_____

_____

List the 5 states that picked Red or Sugar Maple for their state tree:

_____

_____

_____

_____

_____

Find this state on page **5** and use a different color to fill it in.

What is the capital city of this state?
_____

# CREATIVE WRITING

In the space below, write a poem, short story, or a unique history tid-bit about the state tree. If this tree is in your state, and in season, try taping a leaf to this page and press it in the book!

_____
_____
_____
_____
_____
_____
_____

List the different colors of this tree in each season:

**Winter:** _____

**Spring:** _____

**Summer:** _____

**Autumn:** _____

How tall does this tree grow?
_____

What is the average diameter of the tree's trunk?
_____

What is the average lifespan of this tree?
_____

List the sources you used to research this tree:

Books: _____

Websites: _____

Other sources: _____

# WYOMING

The state tree is:
## Plains Cottonwood

Find the botanical name: _____

   List any other names by which this tree is known: _____

_____

Is this tree deciduous or coniferous (evergreen)? _____

Does this tree produce flowers? _____ Which season? _____

   Does this tree produce fruit? _____ What kind? _____

Is this tree's trunk hardwood or softwood? _____

List some items made from the wood of this state tree: _____

_____

_____

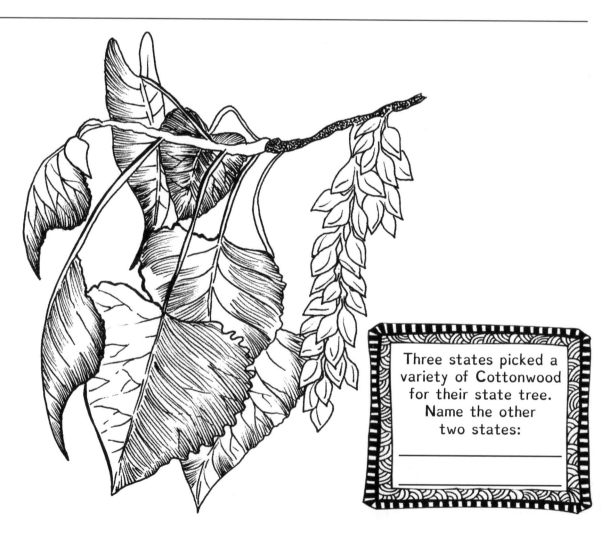

Three states picked a variety of Cottonwood for their state tree. Name the other two states:

_____

_____

124

Find this state on page **5** and use a different color to fill it in.

What is the capital city of this state?

_____

# CREATIVE WRITING

In the space below, write a poem, short story, or a unique history tid-bit about the state tree. If this tree is in your state, and in season, try taping a leaf to this page and press it in the book!

_____

_____

_____

_____

_____

_____

_____

List the different colors of this tree in each season:

**Winter:** _____

**Spring:** _____

**Summer:** _____

**Autumn:** _____

How tall does this tree grow?

_____

What is the average diameter of the tree's trunk?

_____

What is the average lifespan of this tree?

List the sources you used to research this tree:

Books: _____

Websites: _____

Other sources: _____

# CREATIVE ARTS

Fill in the missing parts. Write the name of each tree from this section:

# CREATIVE ARTS

Draw your favorite tree from this section. Use your imagination to draw the tree in its natural habitat. Add a house, forest, or animals!

THE Thinking TREE

PUBLISHING COMPANY

Sarah Janisse Brown

FUNSCHOOLINGBOOKS.COM

Made in the USA
Middletown, DE
09 March 2022